Scoring High

Iowa Tests of Basic Skills®

A Test Prep Program for ITBS

Book 2

SRA

A Division of The McGraw-Hill Companies

Columbus, Ohio
Chicago, Illinois

www.sra4kids.com

SRA/McGraw-Hill

*A Division of The **McGraw·Hill** Companies*

Book 2

On Your Way to Scoring High
On the **Iowa Tests of Basic Skills**®

Name _____

S

- ○ pot
- ○ pan
- ◉ bowl
- ○ dish

 **TIPS**   **Look at the picture and all the answer choices.**

1

- ○ await
- ○ listen
- ○ arrange
- ◉ compute ✓

3

- ◉ retrieve ✓
- ◉ revolve
- ○ repeat
- ○ resist

2

- ◉ damaged ✓
- ○ strong
- ○ healthy
- ○ replaced

4

- ○ king
- ○ rule
- ◉ crown ✓
- ○ royal

GO

1

5

- ○ messy ✓
- ○ neat
- ○ sleepy
- ○ awake

6

- ○ date
- ○ month
- ○ clock
- ○ calendar ✓

7

- ○ balance ✓
- ○ swim
- ○ eat
- ○ clap

8

- ○ look
- ○ listen
- ○ crawl ✓
- ○ carry

9

- ○ program
- ○ pennant ✓
- ○ sports
- ○ crowd

10

- ○ hold
- ○ point ✓
- ○ drop
- ○ catch

11

- ○ study ✓
- ○ play
- ○ argue
- ○ visit

STOP

S

Part of a shirt is a …

○ zipper   ○ collar   ○ belt   ○ brim ✓

1

To go someplace is to …

○ prepare   ○ raise   ◉ travel ✓   ○ enjoy

2

A sad face is a …

○ smile   ○ grin   ◉ frown ✓   ○ share

3

To buy something is to …

○ find   ○ return   ○ repair   ◉ purchase ✓

4

Something that just happened is …

○ next   ◉ coming   ◉ recent ✓   ○ distant

5

To tell someone what to do is to …

○ call   ○ order ✓   ○ offend   ◉ contact

GO

6

Something that has been fixed is …

○ repeated   ○ released   ◉ repaired ✓   ○ received

7

A large container for water is a …

◉ barrel   ○ chest   ○ basket   ◉ carton ✓

8

Part of a leg is a …

○ wrist   ◉ knee ✓   ○ finger   ○ shoulder

9

To jump is to …

○ fall   ○ step   ○ skip   ◉ leap ✓

STOP

Test Yourself: Vocabulary

S1

○ feel
○ sense
◉ listen ✓
◉ view

3

○ box
○ stamp
○ sign
◉ envelope ✓

1

○ angry
○ lazy
◉ funny ✓
○ noisy

4

○ knife
◉ razor ✓
○ scissors
○ saw

2

◉ drive ✓
○ float
○ soar
○ sail

5

○ light
◉ plug ✓
○ battery
○ shine

STOP

S2

To find something is to …

○ lose   ○ replace   ○ dismiss   ◉ discover ✓

6

A covering for a window is a …

○ wall   ○ door   ○ carpet   ◉ curtain ✓

7

To be silly is to be …

○ grim   ○ weak   ◉ foolish ✓   ○ scared

8

When you are sick you are …

○ kind   ○ soft   ○ quick   ◉ ill ✓

9

A noise you make when you sleep is a …

○ cough   ◉ snore ✓   ○ yell   ○ shout

10

A wolf's noise is a …

◉ howl ✓   ○ roar   ○ grunt   ○ hiss

GO ➡

11

To be smart is to be …

○ dull   ○ alone   ○ wicked   ◉ bright ✓

12

To hold something tightly is to …

○ tie   ○ slide   ◉ grip ✓   ○ choose

13

Something that is very dirty is …

◉ rare   ○ spotless   ○ shiny   ◉ filthy ✓

14

To want something is to …

○ avoid   ◉ desire ✓   ○ replace   ◉ borrow

STOP

Word Analysis
Lesson 2a **Word Analysis**

S1

bend	bring	beach
○	◉	○

TIPS If you aren't sure which answer is correct, take your best guess.

1

trick	soft	strap
○	○	○

2

eating	end	ear
○	○	○

3

all	open	age
○	○	○

4

idea	early	easy
○	○	○

5

shell	stump	spell
○	○	○

6

east	ocean	enter
○	○	○

7

there	table	thank
○	○	○

8

stripe	island	improve
○	○	○

GO

S2

| hope | ○ | ○ | ○ |

9

| run | ○ | ○ | ○ |

10

| tag | ○ | ○ | ○ |

11

| down | ○ | ○ | ○ |

12

| fair | ○ | ○ | ○ |

13

| luck | ○ | ○ | ○ |

S3

| club | ○ | ○ | ○ |

14

| stop | ○ | ○ | ○ |

15

| past | ○ | ○ | ○ |

16

| hair | ○ | ○ | ○ |

17

| toast | ○ | ○ | ○ |

18

| hide | ○ | ○ | ○ |

GO →

9

S4

tent   come   mail
○   ○   ○

S5

p__t   a   u   o
       ○   ○   ○

19

cup   dark   green
○   ○   ○

24

b__ke   a   o   i
       ○   ○   ○

20

plate   dress   farm
○   ○   ○

25

n__l   ai   oa   ea
       ○   ○   ○

21

jump   work   found
○   ○   ○

26

c__nt   i   e   a
       ○   ○   ○

22

long   hear   best
○   ○   ○

27

b__rd   ou   oa   ai
       ○   ○   ○

23

men   cook   girl
○   ○   ○

28

s__ck   i   a   o
       ○   ○   ○

GO

S6

long   wrong   strong
○   ○   ○

S7

| fast | ly | er | ous |

○   ○   ○

29

stool   fool   school
○   ○   ○

34

| enjoy | able | es | ion |

○   ○   ○

30

slow   know   throw
○   ○   ○

35

| help | es | ly | ing |

○   ○   ○

31

light   mind   myself
○   ○   ○

36

| quick | ing | ly | ist |

○   ○   ○

32

stamp   hand   lamb
○   ○   ○

33

sign   bugs   gold
○   ○   ○

STOP

S1

unit   until   upset
○   ○   ○

TIPS   **If you aren't sure which answer is correct, take your best guess.**

1

slept   strap   search
○   ○   ○

2

claim   slide   call
○   ○   ○

3

cry   drip   climb
○   ○   ○

4

are   ape   and
○   ○   ○

5

blind   drill   train
○   ○   ○

6

make   swim   well
○   ○   ○

7

island   air   oven
○   ○   ○

8

loaf   rice   bride
○   ○   ○

GO ➤

S2 down ○ ○ ○

S3 sand ○ ○ ○

9 jar ○ ○ ○

14 hot ○ ○ ○

10 sing ○ ○ ○

15 lip ○ ○ ○

11 nap ○ ○ ○

16 set ○ ○ ○

12 lass ○ ○ ○

17 sat ○ ○ ○

13 hog ○ ○ ○

18 rub ○ ○ ○

GO

S4

hint   mat   dark

○   ○   ○

S5

f__ce   e   a   i

•   ○   ○   ○

19

rich   love   most

○   ○   ○

24

p__ny   a   i   o

○   ○   ○

20

round   loan   mug

○   ○   ○

25

p__rk   e   a   i

○   ○   ○

21

ship   more   lack

○   ○   ○

26

m__lk   o   e   i

○   ○   ○

22

help   lean   sold

○   ○   ○

27

h__rse   a   o   u

○   ○   ○

23

lick   sand   mile

○   ○   ○

28

gr__nd   ou   oo   oi

○   ○   ○

GO

S6

cart	comb	cord
○	○	○

29

knock	king	kept
○	○	○

30

want	wood	wrap
○	○	○

31

gold	grand	ghost
○	○	○

32

nest	night	navy
○	○	○

33

scissors	start	slip
○	○	○

S7

build	ly	ist	er
	○	○	○

34

jump	ly	ed	or
	○	○	○

35

act	or	ly	es
	○	○	○

36

glad	ist	ly	ion
	○	○	○

STOP

S1

top   dog   kiss
○   ○   ○

1

left   call   block
○   ○   ○

2

stripe   bright   cry
○   ○   ○

3

chip   this   shift
○   ○   ○

4

also   until   ending
○   ○   ○

5

tribe   change   sting
○   ○   ○

6

crib   float   bread
○   ○   ○

7

upper   even   added
○   ○   ○

8

barns   sharp   smart
○   ○   ○

9

oven   inside   orange
○   ○   ○

GO ➡

S2

hall			
	○	○	○

S3

fool			
	○	○	○

10

junk			
	○	○	○

15

like			
	○	○	○

11

hair			
	○	○	○

16

need			
	○	○	○

12

rake			
	○	○	○

17

rust			
	○	○	○

13

bed			
	○	○	○

18

wake			
	○	○	○

14

lap			
	○	○	○

19

both			
	○	○	○

GO ▶

S4

boot   road   loud

○   ○   ○

20

rope   stop   black

○   ○   ○

21

blue   rub   hope

○   ○   ○

22

top   booth   most

○   ○   ○

23

noise   high   pour

○   ○   ○

24

last   paid   load

○   ○   ○

25

rain   hard   with

○   ○   ○

26

hike   boil   hole

○   ○   ○

S5

s__p   oi   oa   ea

        ○   ○   ○

27

ch__r   ea   oa   ai

        ○   ○   ○

28

sk__rt   o   i   e

        ○   ○   ○

29

b__ll   o   a   u

        ○   ○   ○

GO ➡

30

w__rm   o   a   u
        ⊘   ○   ○

31

v__st   i   a   e
      ○   ○   ⊘

32

pl__ne   a   o   u
       ⊘   ○   ○

33

d__r   oi   oo   oa
      ○   ⊘   ○

S6

score   sort   scene
   ○   ○   ○

34

half   herd   salt
   ○   ○   ○

35

bring   climb   smart
   ○   ○   ○

36

winter   swing   write
   ○   ○   ○

37

high   horn   gift
   ○   ○   ○

38

world   knight   kindest
   ○   ○   ○

39

finger   kindest   knife
   ○   ○   ○

40

cart   calf   cold
   ○   ○   ○

GO ➤

Test Yourself: Word Analysis

S7

art	ist	ly	able
	○	○	○

41

strong	able	ous	er
	○	○	○

42

catch	est	es	ly
	○	○	○

43

slow	on	ist	est
	○	○	○

44

play	ed	ly	es
	○	○	○

45

near	es	ly	ist
	○	○	○

46

say	ist	es	ing
	○	○	○

STOP

Unit 3 Reading

Lesson 3a **Pictures**

S

After school, Willie went to the _____.

○ park   ○ pool   ⦸ store   ○ beach

Look at the picture. It will help you answer the questions.

1 Pat was _____ with the dog.

  ○ eating   ⦸ playing   ○ reading   ○ swimming

2 She threw the _____ to the dog.

  ⦸ stick   ○ ball   ○ rock   ○ shoe

3 The dog has a black _____.

  ○ foot   ○ tail   ⦸ ear   ○ spots

STOP

21

1 Gary is working in the _____ .

     ◯ garden   ◯ garage   ◯ kitchen   ◯ basement

2 He is using a _____ .

     ◯ shovel   ◯ rake   ◯ fence   ◯ saw

3 A _____ is watching him.

     ◯ dog   ◯ horse   ◯ bird   ◯ frog

4 Gary _____ gardening.

     ◯ calls   ◯ watches   ◯ waits   ◯ enjoys

STOP

It was Saturday. Mr. and Mrs. Long woke the children early. They were going to a parade. They would stand where they could see the parade well.

S   Where is the Long family going?

- ○ To the zoo
- ⊘ To a parade
- ○ To the beach

Look back at the story to find the answer.

Uri's mother came home from work one day with a strange-looking machine. She told Uri it was a fax machine, something she used for her job.

His mother plugged the fax machine into the phone line and the electric outlet. Uri wanted to send a note to his father at work. His mother put the note in the fax machine, and off went a copy to Uri's father.

Later, Uri heard the phone ring. He was surprised when the fax machine answered the phone. Uri was even more surprised when a note from his father came out of the machine. It said, "Hi, Uri. I'll be home soon."

1   Who came home first?

- ⊘ Uri
- ○ Uri's mother
- ○ Uri's father

2   What must Uri's father have at work?

- ○ A television
- ⊘ A fax machine
- ○ A computer

3   How does a fax send information from one place to another?

- ○ Through the television antenna
- ○ Through electric lines
- ⊘ Through telephone lines

23

Jill was very happy. Her teacher was taking the class to the city library.

"Please keep quiet inside," the teacher told them. "A library is a quiet place."

One part of the library seemed special to Jill. It was a quiet little nook in the children's section. The corner had a soft blue chair that faced a large window. The window looked out on the street. You could see the park across the street.

"We call that the 'catbird seat,'" the librarian told Jill. "We call it that for a funny reason. It would be a fine spot for a cat to watch for birds."

Jill looked out the window. She could see many birds in the park. Jill could also see people walking their dogs.

The library soon became Jill's favorite place. She went there often after school. It was quiet and relaxing. Jill could always find something to read there.

Jill was happiest when no one was in the catbird seat. When she sat there, she could look up from the book she was reading. From her special place, she could see what was happening outside. She could see drivers making deliveries and people talking. But inside the library, it was very quiet.

4 **How did Jill discover the library?**

- ○ She saw it from the park.
- ○ She lived nearby.
- ⊘ She went on a class trip.

5 **What did the teacher want the students to remember?**

- ○ To return books
- ⊘ To be quiet
- ○ To look at the city

6 **What does Jill do in the library?**

- ⊘ Read
- ○ Play
- ○ Eat

7 **How does Jill feel when she is in the catbird seat?**

- ○ Lonely
- ○ Angry
- ⊘ Peaceful

8 **Which of these is in the nook?**

- ⊘ A blue chair
- ○ A soft carpet
- ○ A nice lamp

GO

Frogs are nature's clowns. They do funny things like hop and croak. They even look funny.

A horned frog is hard to find. It has rough, dark skin. It burrows deep into the ground. Only its big round eyes show.

You can't miss the red-eyed tree frog. Its body is bright green with blue stripes. This frog has orange toes, a yellow belly, and red eyes.

The poison dart frog is colorful too. It is blue and green with large black spots. Its skin is like a flashing sign. The sign says, "Do not eat me. I am poisonous."

When you drive a car, a yellow light means slow down. With the yellow frog, it means stop! Bright colors are like warnings. This frog is not just poisonous. It tastes bad too.

The grass frog has a strange habit. When it calls another frog, its cheeks fill with air. The cheeks get so big they look like chewing-gum bubbles.

Many frogs look strange. Even so, they are important creatures. They eat lots of bugs that might cause us problems.

9 **Which frog looks like it is blowing bubbles?**

- ⊘ Horned frog
- ○ Yellow frog
- ○ Grass frog

10 **Which of these is a warning sign?**

- ○ Round eyes
- ⊘ Bright colors
- ○ Rough skin

11 **How do frogs help us?**

- ⊘ They eat bugs.
- ○ They clean the air.
- ○ They make honey.

12 **What does the horned frog do?**

- ○ Hops very far
- ○ Makes a funny noise
- ⊘ Burrows into the ground

13 **What sound does a frog make?**

- ⊘ Croak
- ○ Buzz
- ○ Hum

Mr. Del Rio's students wrote a letter. They sent it to the mayor of Lake City. They hoped the mayor would write back. They wanted to have a parade.

On Thursday during math, there was a knock on the door. A tall man walked in. To everyone's surprise, it was the mayor. Mr. Del Rio did not know what to say. Finally, he said, "Welcome, your honor."

The mayor greeted the class. He thanked them for their letter. He liked their idea for a wild-animal parade. It would be a good teaching tool. People could learn about animals that needed protection.

He talked to the students. He asked questions. He wanted to know what animals they would be. They told him there were lots of choices. Butterflies, turtles, and even bears needed help.

"What will you be?" Mr. Del Rio asked the mayor.

"With legs like these?" Mr. Sanders said. "I'll probably be a stork."

1 **What did the students' letter ask?**

- ⊘ If they could have a parade
- ○ What animals needed their help
- ○ If the mayor would visit their school

2 **Why would the mayor make a good stork?**

- ○ He has the voice of a bird.
- ⊘ He has long legs.
- ○ He has a sharp nose.

3 **Where was the school?**

- ○ Del Rio
- ⊘ Lake City
- ○ Sanders

4 **On which day did the mayor visit?**

- ○ Monday
- ○ Tuesday
- ⊘ Thursday

5 **What name did Mr. Del Rio call the mayor?**

- ⊘ Your honor
- ○ Mr. President
- ○ Good sir

GO

Writers are always looking for ideas. Marjorie Rawlings was a writer. She took a trip to Florida. The place filled her with ideas. This made Rawlings very happy. She decided to move there.

Rawlings bought an orange grove. She moved into an old farmhouse. She worked hard. She learned about growing oranges. She wrote about what she learned.

One of her stories was called *The Yearling*. It took place in Florida. It was about a farm boy and his pet deer. The book was a big success. It won a famous prize. Later, the story became a movie.

Rawlings also wrote *Cross Creek*. This story was about life on a Florida orange grove. Rawlings described the weather, the insects, the farming, and the neighbors.

Life was sometimes hard on the orange grove. Still, Rawlings loved her new home. It filled her with peace and gave her more ideas for stories.

6 What does the story say about writers?

- ○ They like to eat oranges.
- ⊘ They look for ideas.
- ○ They are rich.

7 How are *The Yearling* and *Cross Creek* alike?

- ○ They are about farm children.
- ○ They tell about growing oranges.
- ⊘ They take place in the same state.

8 The book *The Yearling* was a great success. What does this mean?

- ○ The book was long.
- ⊘ Many people read the book.
- ○ Marjorie Rawlings was on television.

9 What might you read about in *Cross Creek*?

- ○ What the ocean is like
- ⊘ How to grow oranges
- ○ Why people build houses

GO →

Nicole had always liked fireworks. She loved to see the different colors in the sky. Red and green and blue sparkles high above her—it was a sight! Nicole's favorite time of the year was July 4 because of the fireworks.

On July 2, Nicole's father told her that he had a surprise for her.

"What is it?" asked Nicole.

"If I told you, it wouldn't be a surprise!" her dad laughed. "But I will tell you this. It has something to do with camping."

Two days later, Nicole and her father got their sleeping bags and camping gear. Nicole worried that they would miss the fireworks that night. They got into the car and drove a short distance to a park. They then hiked up some hills.

"I don't think there will be any fireworks out here," Nicole said.

Her father just pointed ahead. There was a clearing at the edge of a hill. From it, they could see their whole city below them.

"We'll have the best view of the fireworks from up here," Nicole's dad grinned.

10 **What is the story's surprise?**

- ○ A ride in the car to a park
- ⊘ A special place to see fireworks
- ○ A long hike up some hills

11 **What is not something Nicole does in this story?**

- ○ Hiking in the hills
- ○ Camping outside the city
- ⊘ Lighting fireworks

12 **What is a "clearing" in the story?**

- ⊘ An open area
- ○ The night sky
- ○ A surprise

13 **How many days before July 4 did Nicole's father tell her he had a surprise?**

- ⊘ 2 days
- ○ 3 days
- ○ 4 days

14 **What is this story mostly about?**

- ○ Hiking and camping as a family
- ⊘ A special July 4 surprise
- ○ A girl getting to know her father

28

S  Mark is putting on his _____.

    ○ coat   ○ hat   ∅ shoe   ○ shirt

 **Look at the picture. It will help you answer the questions.**

1 Lucy and her brother, Noah, are at the _____.

    ○ beach   ○ store   ∅ zoo   ○ library

2 Noah enjoys looking at the _____.

    ∅ animals   ○ fish   ○ trees   ○ flowers

3 The children _____ treats to the monkeys.

    ○ receive   ○ remove   ○ send   ∅ toss

GO

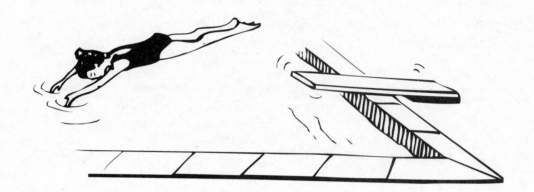

4 Christa likes to go to the _____ .

　○ ocean　　　○ river　　○ pool　　　○ lake

5 She enjoys _____ most of all.

　○ diving　　　○ running　　○ jumping　　○ swimming

6 After she dives in, Christa will climb _____ the pool.

　○ into　　　○ through　　○ around　　○ out of

7 On hot days, swimming helps Christa feel _____ .

　○ cool　　　○ warm　　○ busy　　○ kind

GO

8 Donna stood on the _____.

    ○ hall   ○ porch   ○ steps   ○ corner

9 She is _____ for the bus.

    ○ waiting   ○ riding   ○ calling   ○ visiting

10 Her _____ is with her.

    ○ dog   ○ team   ○ friend   ○ teacher

11 They think the day will be _____.

    ○ snowy   ○ rainy   ○ sunny   ○ cold

STOP

Today was moving day for Grandma. Mom and I were helping. Some neighbors helped too.

Grandma was in a cheerful mood. "Good-bye to the old," she said. "Hello to the new." I was surprised because she didn't seem sad.

All of Grandma's things were packed. Mom lifted the big boxes into the van. I helped with the smaller boxes. Grandma stood on the front porch. "There are lots of memories here, Vicky," she said.

"Harold and I planted our first garden here," she said.

I had my own memories. "Olga had puppies here," I said.

Mom dusted off her hands. "I was born here," she said.

Grandma nodded. "It happened so fast," she said. "By the time the doctor arrived, you were already here."

We got into the van and pulled away from the house. Nobody spoke for a while. I thought I would cry. Then Grandma turned around.

"Have you seen my new house?" she asked. "I think you will like it." I could tell she was ready to make new memories.

12 How does Grandma feel in this story?

- ○ Worried
- ○ Happy
- ○ Sad

13 Who was born in the old house?

- ○ Mom
- ○ Grandma
- ○ Harold

14 Who is Olga?

- ○ A dog
- ○ A cat
- ○ A friend

15 Why was Vicky surprised?

- ○ Because the new house was nice
- ○ Because Grandma wasn't sad
- ○ Because her mother was born in the old house

16 Who is telling this story?

- ○ Vicky
- ○ Grandma
- ○ Vicky's mother

GO

Nick loved going to Uncle Fred's house. Uncle Fred had his own library. The shelves for books covered the walls. They reached from floor to ceiling.

Some of the books had things hidden in them. Nick liked looking inside the books. He pretended he was a detective. He tried to figure out what the things meant. Once, Nick pulled a large book from the shelf. He put it on the table and opened it. Inside was a sheet of paper.

At the top of the paper were two words: "Family Tree." Underneath were rows of lines. On each line was a name.

"What's this?" Nick asked.

"It's our family tree," said Uncle Fred. "It shows how our family started. It tells who married whom and what children they had."

Nick examined the paper. It did not look like a tree to him.

"So, am I a leaf or a piece of fruit?" he asked. Uncle Fred just laughed.

17 **Where does this story take place?**

- ○ Under a tree in the yard
- ⌀ In the library of a house
- ○ In a park

18 **What does Nick do at Uncle Fred's house?**

- ○ He spends his time reading.
- ⌀ He pretends to be a detective.
- ○ He hides in the bookshelves.

19 **What does a family tree show?**

- ○ Who was in the library
- ○ What kinds of trees people like
- ⌀ All the people in a family

20 **Where did Uncle Fred keep his books?**

- ⌀ On shelves
- ○ In boxes
- ○ On the floor

21 **What did Uncle Fred laugh at?**

- ○ The family tree
- ⌀ Nick's joke
- ○ A large book

GO

Hawaii is a beautiful place. Many people visit there. Most people swim and sit on the beach. Some people go for another reason. They go to visit Hawaii's national park. They want to see the world's largest volcano.

Mauna Loa is a mountain volcano. It rises high above the sea. The volcano pours out lava, which is melted rock. The lava does not come from the top. It comes from the sides. The lava cools and becomes hard rock. More rock means more land. This explains Mauna Loa's nickname. It is "Great Builder." One time, the lava did not stop. It poured out for a year and a half!

Near Mauna Loa is Kilauea. Kilauea is also a volcano. It is small but very busy. People enjoy watching it. They carry flashlights and stand on the shore. Kilauea's bright red lava glows in the darkness. Sometimes it even reaches the ocean. The lava makes the water boil. Watching Hawaii's volcanoes is very exciting.

22 **Which answer is true about Mauna Loa?**

○ It is a small volcano that makes lots of steam.
∅ It's the biggest volcano of all.
○ It is a part of many movies.

23 **Why is Mauna Loa called "Great Builder"?**

○ Its rocks are used for buildings.
∅ It keeps making more land.
○ Its shape looks like a tower.

24 **What happens when lava reaches the ocean?**

∅ The water boils.
○ Waves are made.
○ The wind blows.

25 **When do people like to watch Kilauea?**

○ In the morning
○ At noon
∅ At night

26 **What do you know about lava from the story?**

○ It moves very fast.
∅ It is hot.
○ It floats in water.

STOP

Unit 4

Listening
Lesson 5a **Listening Skills**

S

 ◯

 ◯

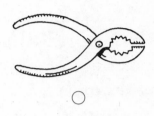 ◯

1

 ◯

 ◯

 ◯

2

 ◯

 ◯

 ◯

3

 ◯

 ◯

 ◯

GO ➡

4

○   ○   ○

5

○   ○   ○

6

○   ○   ○

7

○   ○   ○

STOP

1

2

3

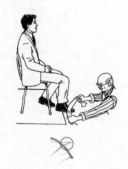  

4

GO ▶

5

○   ○   ○

6

○   ○   ○

7

 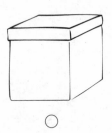 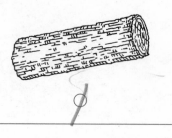

○   ○   ○

8

SINGS THE TUNE

SEE   **SET**   **GET**

 ○   ○

STOP

Test Yourself: Listening

S

A	S	D
○	⊘	○

1

○   ○   ○

2

 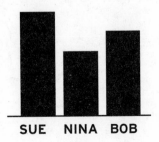 

○   ○   ○

3

○   ○   ○

GO ▶

4

CMEA

ACME	MACE	CAME
○	○	

5

○   ○   ○

6

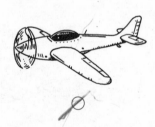

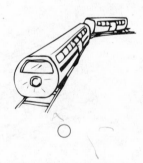

○   ○   ○

7

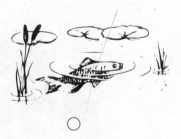

○   ○   ○

GO ▶

8

 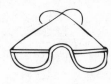 

○ ○ ○

9

○ ○ ○

10

 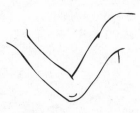 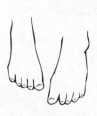

○ ○ ○

11

KEN **BHKVSEGNJP**

SUE **TED** **KEN**

○ ○ ○

STOP

S

○   ⌀   ○

 **TIPS**   Listen carefully while you look at the pictures or words.

1

○   ○   ○

2

○   ○   ○

3

○   ○   ○

4

○   ◸   ◗

○   ○   ○

 **STOP**

S

eight ○   seven ○   number ○   twelve ○

1

horse ○   farm ○   cow ○   pig ○

2

with ○   beside ○   travel ○   before ○

3

rain ○   snow ○   fog ○   wet ○

4

rug ○   desk ○   chair ○   table ○

S1

wer'e   famous   garden
○   ○   ○

S2

cooler   shade   trea
○   ○   ○

Look at the words while you listen to the sentence.

Remember, look for the word that is spelled wrong.

1

cleaned   kitchn   floor
○   ○   ○

4

open   wendow   later
○   ○   ○

2

wal   made   bricks
○   ○   ○

5

haire   looks   pretty
○   ○   ○

3

tell   neww   story
○   ○   ○

6

threw   shell   watre
○   ○   ○

STOP

Language
Lesson 7b Spelling

1

bike   rases   park
○   ○   ○

6

made   appel   pie
○   ○   ○

2

pade   new   sheets
○   ○   ○

7

suer   knee   fine
○   ○   ○

3

boats   duks   lake
○   ○   ○

8

didn't   want   aneything
○   ○   ○

4

rideing   horses   birthday
○   ○   ○

9

cood   find   key
○   ○   ○

5

was   clowdy   beach
○   ○   ○

10

kickd   ball   far
○   ○   ○

STOP

S1

  ○   This is my cousin.

  ∅   he just moved here from

  ○   a small town in Iowa.

S2

  ○   It is raining so hard

  ∅   that i don't think we can

  ○   rake the leaves.

 **The first word in a sentence and important words in a sentence should be capitalized.**

1

  ∅   The art by grandma Moses

  ○   showed a group of people

  ○   enjoying a snowy winter day.

3

  ○   Once a month we go to

  ○   the community gardens, and

  ∅   i pull weeds and plant seeds.

2

  ○   The forest was Clem's

  ∅   favorite place to go, he

  ○   liked the smell of the trees.

4

  ○   Guests at Sadie's house

  ∅   know that sunday afternoons

  ○   are spent watching movies.

 STOP

1

○ When Miss Weeks was a

○ girl, people called her red. Can

○ you guess the color of her hair?

2

○ Our cat seemed sick on

○ Wednesday. We called the pet

○ hospital and spoke to dr. Riley.

3

○ My uncle Dirk lives in

○ montana. He runs a farm

○ with a hundred acres of land.

4

○ Randy and silas asked their

○ geography teacher how many

○ different countries there are.

5

○ The best Mexican food

○ is sold at the taco stand on the

○ south side of alberta street.

6

○ Carly is a year old. when

○ she gets in the car with her

○ parents, she says, "We go!"

STOP

S1

○ Our neighbor's dog had
○ puppies last week. Mother
○ said I can have one of them

S2

○ Stop The ice is very thin
○ there. Let's skate closer to
○ the shore where it is thicker.

Look for punctuation at the end of a sentence first. Then look for punctuation inside the sentence.

1

○ I have been outside of
○ the US only one time. Last fall
○ my family drove to Canada.

3

○ I had Mr. Amundson as my
○ kindergarten teacher He taught
○ our class lots of different songs.

2

○ After weeks of planning, our
○ store was ready. Our first big
○ sale would be on June 18 2002.

4

○ Kelly was busy training her
○ new puppy. When the puppy
○ behaved, Kelly said, Good dog.

STOP

1

○ When the rain stops, do you

○ want to take a walk We can

○ wear raincoats just in case.

2

○ Have you read any books

○ by JRR Tolkien? He is

○ one of my favorite authors.

3

○ August 21 1959 is an

○ important date for Hawaii. It

○ joined the U.S. on that day.

4

○ Dad fixes soup whenever I

○ get sick. He says it has special

○ powers to make me well again.

5

○ James did not think he could

○ walk. His mother gave him

○ a smile and said, You can do it.

6

○ Whenever we bake bread,

○ the kitchen smells so good.

○ Can we make some today.

STOP

49

Unit 5

Language

Lesson 10a **Usage and Expression**

S1

○ I and my sister went to

○ the zoo. We saw lots of

○ animals and had a good time.

S2

○ My father takes good

○ care of his kitchen knifes. He

○ sharpens them every day.

Use the meaning of the story to find the answer.

1

○ Once a week the animals get

○ a treat. The dog gets a bone,

○ and the cats gets warm milk.

3

○ Rain poured from the sky

○ like a waterfall. Amazing. It

○ seemed it would never stop.

2

○ There are many womens in

○ my family. Mom has six sisters

○ who have five daughters each.

4

○ The tree planted James at

○ the old family farm. It was an

○ oak to honor his grandfather.

STOP

1

○ The park most closest to
○ my house is Rose City Park.
○ It is only a few blocks away.

2

○ Last year Kit had never
○ been on a plane. This year he
○ has already flied seven times.

3

○ Yesterday Lola's dad will get
○ a new job. He became boss of
○ a computer company.

4

○ I did not watch the movie
○ Mom rented because I seen
○ it last year in the theater.

5

○ Dad changed dinner plans
○ because without no cheese,
○ it is impossible to make pizza.

6

○ It took Ike and me a while to
○ get the campfire going because
○ the matches they were wet.

STOP

51

Test Yourself: Language

S1

○ ○ ⊘

1

○ ⊘ ○

2

○ ○ ○

3

○ ⊘ ○

4

garden   tree   flower   bush

⊘   ○   ○   ○

5

king   rule   crown   royal

○   ⊘   ○   ○ **GO ➡**

S2

sister   feels   beter
○   ○   ⦰

6

played   weth   string
○   ⦰   ○

7

bus   stoped   near
○   ⦰   ○

8

broon   licked   hand
⦰   ○   ○

9

cake   finished   soun
○   ○   ⦰

10

askd   store   open
⦰   ○   ○

11

fire   kepd   warm
○   ⦰   ○

12

buton   came   shirt
⦰   ○   ○

13

only   win   harrd
○   ○   ⦰

14

third   we'v   been
○   ⦰   ○

GO →

S3

○   The fall trip to the

○   pumpkin patch is Trevor's

○   favorite time with uncle Doyle.

15

○   Fred just stared. he could not

○   believe how hard the winter

○   wind was blowing outside.

16

○   Yesterday the new bakery

○   opened. Gilford and i went

○   and bought a bag of bagels.

17

○   After a busy weekend, Abby

○   often finds it hard to wake

○   up on monday morning.

18

○   Thanksgiving Day is not

○   always on the same date. This

○   year it falls on november 22.

19

○   I like playing music for

○   my friends, but i'm shy about

○   playing in front of strangers.

GO ➡

S4

- ○ The author SE Hinton
- ○ wrote a book when she was 16.
- ○ The book became a big hit.

20

- ○ The Kings finished building
- ○ the house in May but waited
- ○ until June 3 1997 to move in.

21

- ○ When I broke a crayon, I
- ○ asked my mom to fix it She
- ○ put it back together with tape.

22

- ○ Excuse me, Vincent said
- ○ clearly. He had to get through
- ○ the crowded bus station.

23

- ○ Why did Mrs. Carmine
- ○ stop singing She had the
- ○ voice of a gifted singer.

24

- ○ It is too loud in here,
- ○ said Luke. The gymnasium
- ○ was filled with shouting fans.

GO

S5

- ○ My brother had threw the
- ○ ball, and it accidentally hit and
- ○ broke one of our windows.

25

- ○ Especially action movies.
- ○ I like an exciting story that
- ○ makes my heart pound.

26

- ○ Andy took me on my
- ○ first fishing trip. Him and I
- ○ had the best time together.

27

- ○ The woman buyed a gift
- ○ for her daughter. She hoped it
- ○ was something the girl wanted.

28

- ○ We needed to make some
- ○ money. I and my brother set up
- ○ a lemonade stand on a hot day.

29

- ○ Them there apples are kind
- ○ of sour, but they sure taste good
- ○ baked in a homemade pie.

STOP

Mathematics Concepts

Lesson 11a **Mathematics Concepts**

S

○   ○   ○

 TIPS   Listen carefully for key words and numbers while you look at the picture.

1

23   39   46
○   ○   ○

2

3 − 2   5 + 2   3 + 2
○   ○   ○

3

$\frac{1}{4}$ $\frac{1}{2}$ $\frac{3}{4}$
○   ○   ○

4

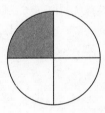

○ 90 minutes

○ 120 minutes

○ 200 minutes

GO →

5

○   ○   ○

8

490

○ Forty-nine

○ Four hundred nine

○ Four hundred ninety

○ Nine hundred four

6

○ light

○ car

○ car

○ car

○ car

○ car

9

| 10 | 20 | 30 | 40 |
| ○ | ○ | ○ | ○ |

7

| 71 | 62 | 78 | 61 |
| ○ | ○ | ○ | ○ |

10

| 5 | 13 | 23 | 32 |
| ○ | ○ | ○ | ○ |

GO

11

○   ○   ○   ○

14

$2.85 $3.40 $4.23 $5.40

○   ○   ○   ○

12

$$4 \; \square \; 2 = 2$$

+   −   ×   =
○   ○   ○   ○

15

___

○   ○   ○   ○

13

○   ○   ○   ○

16

○ $4 + 2 = 2 + 4$

○ $4 - 2 = 2 - 4$

○ $4 \times 2 = 2 \times 4$

STOP

59

1

○   ○   ○   ○

2

$$5 + 3 = 15 \,\square\, 7$$

+   ×   −
○   ○   ○

3

○   ○   ○   ○

4

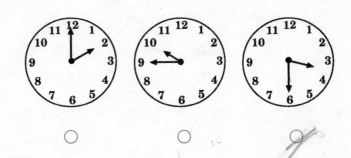

○   ○   ○

5

inch   foot   ounce   pound

○   ○   ○   ○

6

225, ____ , 275, 300, 325

250   255   265   350
○   ○   ○   ○

GO →

7

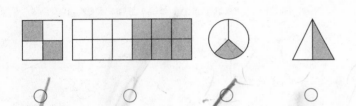

○ ○ ○ ○

10

4¢   20¢   50¢   65¢

○   ○   ○   ○

8

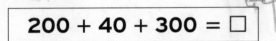

| 200 + 40 + 300 = □ |

243   324   430   540

○   ○   ○   ○

11

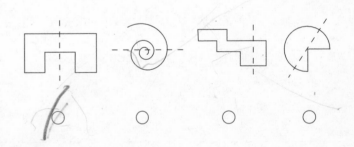

○   ○   ○   ○

9

● 200 + 50 = □

○ 300 + 100 = □

○ 290 + 50 = □

○ 280 + 40 = □

12

30   43   59   68

○   ○   ○   ○

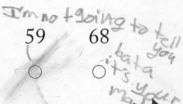

13

- ○ 4 × 3 = 12
- ○ 3 × 5 = 15
- ○ 6 × 3 = 18
- ○ 6 × 4 = 24

16

48 miles per hour   30 miles per hour

10   20   35   40

○   ○   ○   ○

14

- ○ 30 minutes
- ○ 60 minutes
- ○ 100 minutes

17

42 + 49 = ▢

60   70   80   90

○   ○   ○   ○

15

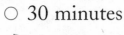

20 − 10 + 3 = ▢

3   7   12   13

○   ○   ○   ○

18

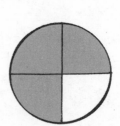

$\frac{1}{3}$ $\frac{2}{3}$ $\frac{3}{4}$ $\frac{5}{6}$

○   ○   ○   ○

STOP

S

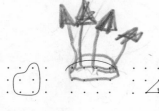

○   ○   ○   ⊘

3

○ flower

○ butterfly

○ butterfly

○ butterfly

⊘ butterfly

○ butterfly

1

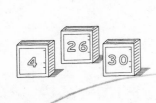

○ 30 − 2 = ⬜ 28

⊘ 30 − 4 = ⬜ 26

○ 26 − 4 = ⬜ 22

○ 20 − 14 = ⬜ 6

4

29   36   48   51

○   ⊘   ○   ○

2

○   ○   ⊘

5

| 501 |

○ Fifty-one

⊘ Five hundred one

○ Five hundred ten

○ One thousand five

GO ▶

6

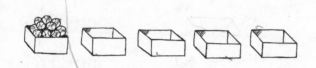

10	25	30	50
○	○	○	⌀

7

6	42	52	80
○	⌀	○	○

8

$$4 \ \square \ 3 = 7$$

+	−	×	=
⌀	○	○	○

9

○	○	○	⌀

10

$3.65 $5.40 $6.10 $6.45

○	⌀	○	○

11

○	⌀	○	○

GO

12

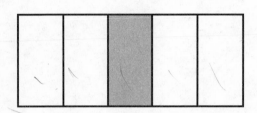

$$\frac{1}{5} \qquad \frac{1}{4} \qquad \frac{1}{3} \qquad \frac{1}{2}$$

○   ○   ○   ○

13

★ ★ ★ ★ ★ ★ ★ ★
★ ★ ★ ★ ★ ★ ★ ★
★ ★ ★ ★ ★ ★ ★ ★
★ ★ ★ ★ ★ ★ ★ ★

○ $2 \times 7 = 14$

○ $3 \times 7 = 21$

○ $6 \times 3 = 18$

○ $7 \times 4 = 28$

14

○ 30 minutes

○ 90 minutes

○ 300 minutes

15

$$10 - 2 + 3 = \square$$

5   7   11   15

○   ○   ○   ○

16

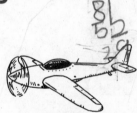

52 miles per hour   **81 miles per hour**

10   20   35   30

○   ○   ○   ○

17

$$18 + 19 = \square$$

40   50   60   90

○   ○   ○   ○

GO →

18

○   ∅   ○   ○

19

$$2 + 7 = 3 \,\square\, 6$$

+   ×   −
∅   ○   ○

20

○   ∅   ○   ○

21

100   120   178   250
○   ○   ○   ○

22

$$100 + 100 + 70 = \square$$

117   170   270   1,017
○   ○   ∅   ○

23

○ $80 + 120 = \square$

○ $70 + 100 = \square$

○ $70 + 110 = \square$

○ $80 + 180 = \square$

STOP

S

2	3	4	N
○	○	○	∅

If you work on scratch paper, be careful when you write the numbers for the problem.

Listen carefully for key words and numbers. Look carefully at any picture that is part of the problem.

1

10	128	12	19
○	○	∅	○

4

7	10	14	17
○	∅	○	○

2

1	3	5	15
○	∅	○	○

5

10	12	19	N
○	○	○	∅

3

3	4	9	15
○	○	○	∅

6

6	7	14	N
○	∅	○	∅

GO →

7

$8 + 4 + 3$

Landra recycles cans for her family. On Monday, she put 8 cans in a box. On Tuesday, she put 4 more in the box. On Wednesday, she put 3 cans in the box. How many cans were in the box all together?

12	13	14	N
○	○	○	⦰

9

5 hours
3 hours
6 hours

Alden is getting ready for a race. He rode his bike 5 hours on Saturday, 3 hours on Sunday, and 6 hours on Monday. How many hours did he ride all together?

12	13	15	N
○	○	○	⦰

8

```
 12
 10
 22
```

Jordie had 10 goldfish. His friend, Aileen, had 12 goldfish. Aileen gave 3 of her goldfish to Jordie. How many goldfish did Jordie and Aileen have in all?

22	23	25	N
⦰	○	○	○

10

Mr. Jeeter had 10 apples in a bag. He put half of the apples in a bowl and the rest in the refrigerator. How many apples did he put in the refrigerator?

3	4	5	6
○	○	⦰	○

STOP

1

Murrell needs 8 stamps to fill one page of his book. How many stamps will he need to fill 4 pages?

⊘ $8 + 8 + 8 + 8 = \square$

○ $8 + 4 = \square$

○ $4 + 4 + 4 + 4 = \square$

2

Nancy put 4 books in a box. Later that day she put 7 more books in the box. Her brother, Fritz, then took 3 books out of the box. How many books were left in the box?

○ $4 + 7 + 3 = \square$

⊘ $4 - 7 - 3 = \square$

○ $4 + 7 - 3 = \square$

3

A group of students took a bus to the zoo. Another group of students took a train to the zoo. How can you find out how many students went to the zoo in all?

○ Subtract the number of students on the bus from the number of students on the train.

○ Add the number of students on the bus to the number of students on the train.

⊘ Subtract the number of students on the train from the number of students on the bus.

4

Cami is 2 inches taller than Reggie. Alice is 3 inches taller than Cami. Who is tallest?

○ Reggie

○ Cami

⊘ Alice

GO

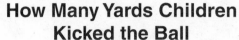

How Many Yards Children Kicked the Ball

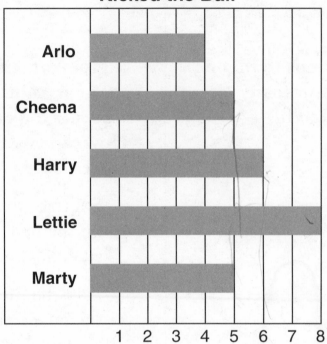

Arlo
Cheena
Harry
Lettie
Marty

1 2 3 4 5 6 7 8

5 How many yards did Arlo kick the ball?

○ 2

○ 3

○ 4

6 Which student kicked the ball 6 yards?

○ Cheena

○ Harry

○ Lettie

7 Which two children kicked the ball the same distance?

○ Harry and Lettie

○ Cheena and Marty

○ Arlo and Cheena

8 How many yards farther did Lettie kick the ball than Cheena?

○ 3

○ 5

○ 8

STOP

S

4

0	2	3	N
○	∅	○	∅

3

5

4	5	9	20
○	○	○	∅

1

4 6

4	6	10	16
○	○	∅	○

4

12   48   4
          8

4	8	9	12
○	○	∅	○

2

15 inches
6 inches

6	9	12	24
○	∅	○	○

5

6 pieces

2	3	4	6
∅	○	○	○

GO ▶

6

Mrs. Lee drew 10 lines on the board. Then she drew 7 more. How many lines did she draw in all?

7	11	17	71
○	○	⌀	○

7

Lisette made 12 sandwiches and 5 salad plates. She gave 3 sandwiches to her friends. How many sandwiches did she have left?

2	3	6	9
○	○	○	⌀

8

Dina's cat weighs 8 pounds, and her dog weighs 15 pounds. How many pounds do the two pets weigh all together?

○ $15 - 8 = \boxed{}$

⌀ $15 + 8 = \boxed{}$

○ $23 - 8 = \boxed{}$

9

45
18

A piece of string is 45 inches long. Mrs. Allen cut 18 inches from the string and used it to tie up some plants. How many inches of string were left?

⌀ $45 - 18 = \boxed{}$

○ $45 + 18 = \boxed{}$

○ $63 - \boxed{} = 18$

10

There are 15 girls in a class. How can you find out how many boys are in the class?

○ Multiply 15 times 2.

○ Add 15 to the number of students in the class.

⌀ Subtract 15 from the number of students in the class.

 GO

Socks	
Hats	
Shoes	
Gloves	
Scarves	

11 How many hats were found?

○ 2

⊘ 3

○ 4

12 Which thing was found the most?

○ Hats

⊘ Socks

○ Shoes

13 How many scarves and gloves were found all together?

○ 3

○ 5

⊘ 8

14 How many more socks than shoes were found?

○ 2

○ 3

⊘ 4

STOP

Mathematics Computation

Lesson 13a **Mathematics Computation**

S1

1	5	6	N
○	○	⊘	○

S2   8 + 1 =

4	7	10	N
○	○	○	⊘

 **Listen carefully to the numbers. Be sure to add.**

1

5	16	17	N
○	○	⊘	○

5

11	12	13	N
⊘	○	○	○

2

7	8	9	N
○	○	⊘	○

6

14	17	18	N
○	○	○	⊘

3

13	16	18	N
○	⊘	○	○

7

34	70	340	N
○	⊘	○	○

4

10	20	21	N
○	○	○	⊘

8

16	17	19	N
○	○	⊘	○

GO →

9 $9 + 2 + 5 + 8 =$

24   29   32   N
○   ○   ○   ○

10 $5 + 9 =$

11   12   16   N
○   ○   ○   ○

11
$$
\begin{array}{r}
302 \\
+ \ 54 \\
\hline
\end{array}
$$

356   365   366   N
○   ○   ○   ○

12
$$
\begin{array}{r}
11 \\
5 \\
+ \ 29 \\
\hline
\end{array}
$$

25   34   45   N
○   ○   ○   ○

13
$$
\begin{array}{r}
24 \\
+ \ 23 \\
\hline
\end{array}
$$

43   47   57   N
○   ○   ○   ○

14
$$
\begin{array}{r}
410 \\
+ \ 290 \\
\hline
\end{array}
$$

600   610   690   N
○   ○   ○   ○

15
$$
\begin{array}{r}
472 \\
+ \ 83 \\
\hline
\end{array}
$$

555   575   577   N
○   ○   ○   ○

16
$$
\begin{array}{r}
846 \\
+ \ 83 \\
\hline
\end{array}
$$

919   929   933   N
○   ○   ○   ○

17
$$
\begin{array}{r}
504 \\
+ \ 59 \\
\hline
\end{array}
$$

529   534   563   N
○   ○   ○   ○

18
$$
\begin{array}{r}
589 \\
+ \ 136 \\
\hline
\end{array}
$$

725   735   753   N
○   ○   ○   ○

STOP

S1

0   1   3   N
○   ○   ○   ○

S2   8 − 6 =

1   3   4   N
○   ○   ○   ○

**Remember, you are supposed to subtract in this lesson.
Eliminate answers that are too big.**

1

2   4   6   N
○   ○   ○   ○

5

5   35   41   N
○   ○   ○   ○

2

0   1   3   N
○   ○   ○   ○

6

10   11   20   N
○   ○   ○   ○

3

7   17   37   N
○   ○   ○   ○

7

10   11   26   N
○   ○   ○   ○

4

29   40   50   N
○   ○   ○   ○

8

20   21   68   N
○   ○   ○   ○

GO ➡

9   16 − 7 =

1	8	9	N
○	○	⊘	○

14   179 − 7 = 172

109	172	177	N
○	⊘	○	○

10   14 − 9 =

4	5	8	N
○	⊘	○	○

15   44 − 27 = 17

3	13	16	N
○	○	○	⊘

11   98 − 45 = 53

33	35	51	N
○	○	○	⊘

16
$$\begin{array}{r} 245 \\ -\ 45 \\ \hline \end{array}$$
200

200	210	300	N
⊘	○	○	○

12   59 − 22 = 37

37	39	42	N
⊘	○	○	○

17
$$\begin{array}{r} 56 \\ -\ 47 \\ \hline \end{array}$$
09

1	2	9	N
○	○	⊘	○

13
$$\begin{array}{r} 248 \\ -\ 42 \\ \hline \end{array}$$
206

106	206	224	N
○	⊘	○	○

18   134 − 6 =

134
6
128

123	128	140	N
○	⊘	○	○

STOP

S1

3	6	8	N
○	○	○	○

S2 $11 - 2 =$

1	3	4	N
○	○	○	○

1

21	26	29	N
○	○	○	○

5
$$581 \\ + 89$$

599	670	699	N
○	○	○	○

2

17	18	19	N
○	○	○	○

6
$$886 \\ + 22$$

882	908	928	N
○	○	○	○

3

13	16	18	N
○	○	○	○

7
$$107 \\ + 44$$

147	154	174	N
○	○	○	○

4

54	75	90	N
○	○	○	○

8
$$77 \\ + 88$$

165	175	185	N
○	○	○	○

STOP

Test Yourself: Mathematics Computation

9

15 45 65 N
○ ○ ○ ○

14 249 − 7 =

202 242 256 N
○ ○ ○ ○

10

29 32 39 N
○ ○ ○ ○

15 44 − 27 =

7 18 27 N
○ ○ ○ ○

11

6 59 69 N
○ ○ ○ ○

16
$$761$$
$$- 16$$

745 746 760 N
○ ○ ○ ○

12

30 31 40 N
○ ○ ○ ○

17
$$37$$
$$- 28$$

7 8 9 N
○ ○ ○ ○

13

7 9 11 N
○ ○ ○ ○

18 127 − 9 =

118 122 129 N
○ ○ ○ ○

STOP

Unit 9

Sources of Information

Lesson 14a Sources of Information

TIPS

Read the question, look at the reference source, and then look at the answer choices.

It may help to read the question a second time.

Hook

Sock

Fan

Bag

Patch

Mask

Whistle

S1 Which picture should be at the very top of the page?

○ Hook

○ Fan

○ Bag

1 Which picture should be between the patch and the whistle?

○ Mask

○ Sock

○ Hook

2 Which picture should be the second one on the page?

○ Fan

○ Bag

○ Patch

3 Which picture should be right after the mask?

○ Whistle

○ Patch

○ Sock

GO ▶

Lesson 14a **Sources of Information**

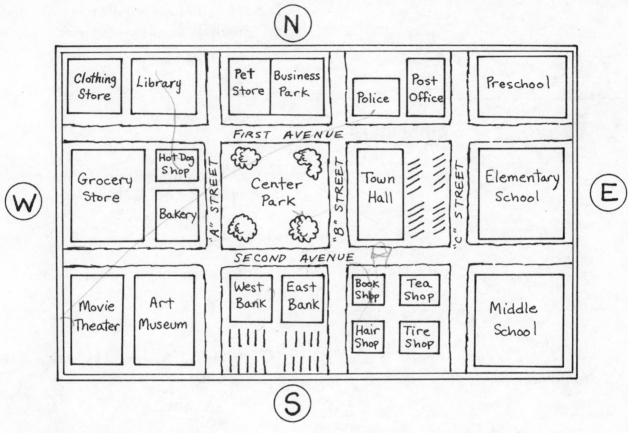

S2 Which is on First Avenue?

○ The bakery

◐ The preschool

○ The tire shop

4 How far is the bookshop from town hall?

◐ One block

○ Two blocks

○ Three blocks

5 Which businesses are across the street from each other?

○ The east bank and the west bank

◐ The library and the hot dog shop

○ The police station and the movie theater

6 Which is closest to B Street?

◐ The pet store

○ The grocery store

○ The art museum

7 Which direction is the center park from the elementary school?

○ East

○ South

◐ West

8 When the bookshop owner goes west on Second Avenue, which does the bookshop owner see first?

○ The tea shop

◐ The east bank

○ The bakery

GO ▶

	**balance** To keep from falling
	binoculars A device used to view distant objects
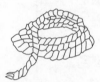	**coil** To wind into rings
	**link** A piece of chain
	**muffler** A heavy scarf for the neck
	**pier** A walkway built from land into the water
	**rescue** To save from danger
	yarn A heavy thread used for knitting or weaving

S3 How do you spell the name of a device used to view distant objects?

- ○ binocolars
- ◐ binoculars
- ○ binoculers

9 Which word best fits in the sentence "The workers walked out on the _____ and unloaded the ship"?

- ○ yarn
- ○ link
- ⊗ pier

10 Which of these would you be most likely to coil?

- ○ A shovel
- ⊗ A hose
- ○ A rake

11 In which season would you be most likely to wear a muffler?

- ○ Spring
- ○ Summer
- ○ Winter

12 Which word fits best in the sentence "The sweater is made of blue _____"?

- ○ yarn
- ○ coil
- ○ link

STOP

Unit 9

Sources of Information

Lesson 14b **Sources of Information**

S1 Which chapter would tell you most about holidays that are still celebrated in China today?

○ Chapter 2

◉ Chapter 4

○ Chapter 6

1 Where should you begin reading to find out how to dress while traveling in China?

○ Page 9

○ Page 11

○ Page 14

2 Which chapter might tell you about schools in China?

○ Chapter 1

○ Chapter 4

○ Chapter 6

3 Where should you begin reading to find out who is the leader of China today?

○ Page 4

◉ Page 7

○ Page 11

4 Where should you begin reading to find out how China got its name?

◉ Page 3

○ Page 7

○ Page 11

5 What might you find in Chapter 5?

○ A picture of Chinese clothing

◉ A map of some cities in China

○ A list of Chinese foods

GO →

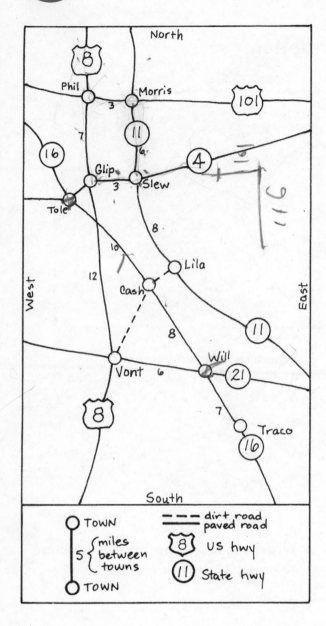

S2 **Which town is located where Highway 4 crosses Highway 8?**

○ Tole

⊘ Glip

○ Slew

6 **Where might you see the highway sign?**

○ Morris

○ Vont   ⑯

⊘ Traco

7 **What kind of road runs from Lila to Slew?**

⊘ A state highway

⊘ A dirt road

○ A U.S. highway

8 **Which is the shortest way from Slew to Phil?**

○ Highway 4, then Highway 8

⊘ Highway 11, then Highway 101

○ Highway 4, then Highway 11

9 **How far is it from Will to Tole?**

○ 8 miles

⊘ 18 miles

○ 21 miles

GO

S3 Which picture should be the first one on the page?

○ Raisins

○ Orange

⊘ Coconut

12 Which picture should be right after the pineapple?

○ Orange

○ Coconut

○ Raisins

10 Which picture should be between the orange and the raisins?

⊘ Pineapple

○ Coconut

○ Grapes

13 Which picture should be between the coconut and the mango?

○ Strawberry

⊘ Grapes

○ Orange

11 Which picture should be the third one on the page?

○ Grapes

○ Mango

○ Orange

14 Which picture should be the last one on the page?

⊘ Strawberry

○ Pineapple

○ Coconut

Test Yourself: Sources of Information

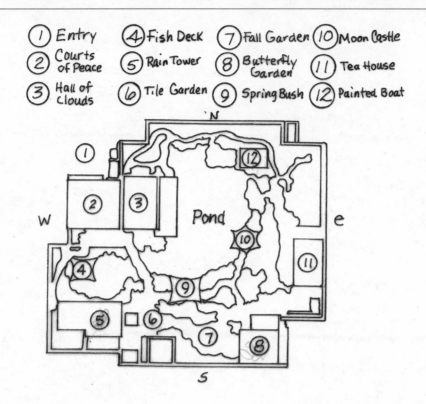

① Entry ④ Fish Deck ⑦ Fall Garden ⑩ Moon Castle
② Courts of Peace ⑤ Rain Tower ⑧ Butterfly Garden ⑪ Tea House
③ Hall of Clouds ⑥ Tile Garden ⑨ Spring Bush ⑫ Painted Boat

1 Which is farthest from the entry?

○ The hall of clouds

○ The fish deck

⊘ The butterfly garden

2 Which would be the hardest to see from the fish deck?

○ The rain tower

⊘ The painted boat

○ The tile garden

3 Which is east of the pond?

⊘ The tea house

○ The hall of clouds

○ The entry

4 What do you pass first when you walk from the rain tower to the butterfly garden?

○ The spring garden

⊘ The tile garden

○ The fall garden

5 Which direction is the painted boat from the tea house?

○ South

○ East

⊘ North

6 Which has water on two sides?

⊘ The moon castle

○ The tea house

○ The hall of clouds

GO ▶

Test Yourself: Sources of Information

carefree
Happy and free from care

closet
A place where things are kept

disturb
To bother someone or something

factory
A building where goods are made

harbor
A place where boats and ships stop to dock

meadow
A grassy pasture or field

rattle
To shake something

summit
The top of a hill or mountain

7 How do you spell a word that means "without cares"?

○ carfree

○ carefre

○ carefree

8 Which word best fits in the sentence "The _____ was filled with wild horses"?

○ meadow

○ summit

○ harbor

9 Where are people most likely to feel carefree?

○ A closet

○ A factory

○ A summit

10 How do you spell the name of a kind of field?

○ medow

○ meadow

○ meddow

11 Which word fits best in the sentence "The ship stayed in the _____ for the night"?

○ harbor

○ factory

○ summit

12 Where would you most likely see a sailor?

○ A factory

○ A harbor

○ A summit

GO

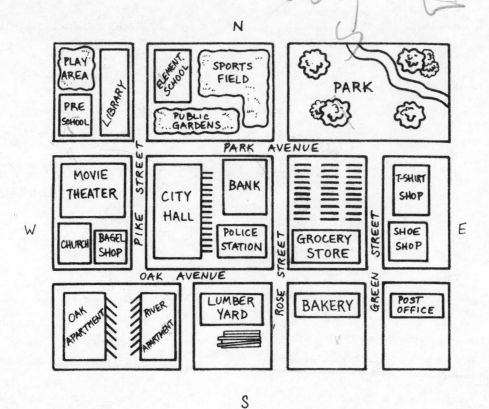

13 How far is the preschool from the park?

○ One block

∅ Two blocks

○ Three blocks

14 Which buildings are across the street from each other?

○ The lumberyard and the police station

○ The bank and city hall

○ The elementary school and the bakery

15 What is closest to Park Avenue?

○ The bakery

○ The bank

○ The bagel shop

16 Which direction is the park from the elementary school?

○ North

○ West

∅ East

17 When the baker leaves the bakery and goes west on Oak Avenue, which does she pass first?

○ The lumberyard

○ The post office

○ The shoe store

18 Which is on Pike Street?

○ The post office

○ The grocery store

○ The bagel shop

GO ➤

Beavers

CONTENTS

19 Where should you begin reading to find out what part of the world beavers live in?

- ○ Page 6
- ○ Page 9
- ○ Page 11

20 Which chapter might tell you how a beaver's home is made?

- ○ Chapter 1
- ○ Chapter 3
- ○ Chapter 5

21 Where should you begin reading to find out what a beaver looks like?

- ○ Page 2
- ○ Page 4
- ○ Page 6

22 Where should you begin reading to find out how beavers raise their young?

- ○ Page 2
- ○ Page 6
- ○ Page 9

23 What might you find in Chapter 5?

- ○ A picture of a beaver's dam
- ○ A map of where beavers live
- ○ A picture of a beaver pup

24 Which chapter would tell you most about what makes a tasty meal for a beaver?

- ○ Chapter 1
- ○ Chapter 3
- ○ Chapter 6

GO ➤

Test Yourself: Sources of Information

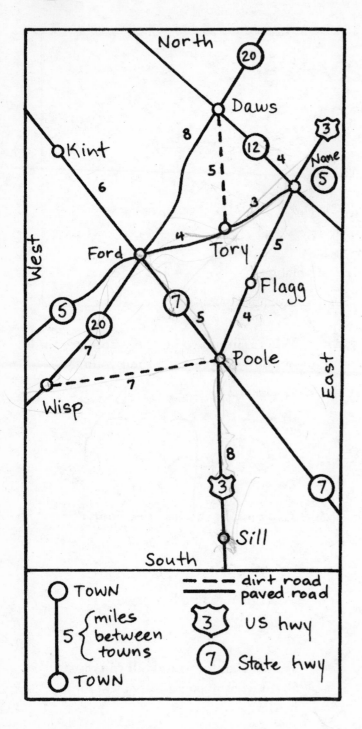

25 Where might you see this highway sign?

○ In Daws

⊘ In Tory

⊘ In Flagg

26 Starting in Sill, Dan drove 8 miles north and 7 miles west. Where did he go?

○ Flagg

○ Tory

⊘ Wisp

27 What kind of road runs between Daws and Tory?

○ A state highway

⊘ A dirt road

○ A U.S. highway

28 Which is the shortest way from Flagg to Daws?

⊘ Highway 3, then Highway 12

○ Highway 7, then Highway 20

○ Highway 3, then Highway 7

29 How far is it from Kint to Poole?

○ 5 miles

○ 6 miles

⊘ 11 miles

Test Practice
Test 1 **Vocabulary**

S1

- ○ pour
- ○ make
- ○ stir
- ○ spill

3

- ○ branch
- ○ trunk
- ○ root
- ○ knot

1

- ○ mow
- ○ rake
- ○ dump
- ○ dig

4

- ○ cup
- ○ basket
- ○ saucer
- ○ glass

2

- ○ wag
- ○ step
- ○ hear
- ○ sniff

5

- ○ damp
- ○ tiny
- ○ slippery
- ○ cool

STOP

S2

To put paper around a box is to ....

   ○ open   ○ ship   ○ wrap   ○ pack

6

Someone who is here is ....

   ○ present   ○ away   ○ unknown   ○ alert

7

Something damaged is ....

   ○ solid   ○ helpful   ○ necessary   ○ broken

8

Clean water is ....

   ○ fast   ○ pure   ○ cloudy   ○ poured

9

To walk into something you didn't see is to ....

   ○ lift   ○ lean   ○ pat   ○ bump

10

To hand something to another person is to ....

   ○ clear   ○ pass   ○ like   ○ speak

STOP

Test Practice

Test 2 Word Analysis

S1

luck   tug   sell
○   ○   ○

5

earth   ugly   and
○   ○   ○

1

mild   rent   cook
○   ○   ○

6

think   drip   clip
○   ○   ○

2

inch   art   open
○   ○   ○

7

snuck   track   brook
○   ○   ○

3

will   twin   nap
○   ○   ○

8

ice   use   eat
○   ○   ○

4

head   stiff   shall
○   ○   ○

9

trust   from   moat
○   ○   ○

GO →

S2 tell

S3 tore

10 hush

15 break

11 late

16 load

12 sick

17 move

13 hop

18 round

14 same

19 reach

GO

S4

mine   lid   raid

○   ○   ○

20

sand   cloth   rent

○   ○   ○

21

chop   load   trap

○   ○   ○

S5

tr__ck   i   a   u

○   ○   ⊘

22

h__se   ou   oa   ue

⊘   ○   ○

23

f__ther   e   o   a

○   ○   ⊘

S6

send   scent   cold

○   ○   ○

24

desk   dust   dumb

○   ○   ○

25

winter   written   wonder

○   ○   ○

S7

| **old** | est | ly | ing |

⊘   ○   ○

26

| **camp** | ly | ist | er |

○   ○   ⊘

27

| **mark** | ly | ing | ist |

○   ⊘   ○

STOP

95

S1 The board has a _____ in it.

   ○ wood   ○ hole   ○ nail   ○ scratch

1 Roger is looking under the _____.

   ○ table   ○ chair   ○ bed   ○ dresser

2 His dog, Tiger, is _____ somewhere.

   ○ hiding   ○ running   ○ begging   ○ barking

3 Roger will be _____ when he finds Tiger.

   ○ early   ○ late   ○ sad   ○ happy

4 Alida borrowed lots of _____.

   ○ shoes   ○ books   ○ videos   ○ toys

5 She _____ to read last year.

   ○ learned   ○ tried   ○ called   ○ lost

6 Alida is waiting for the _____ to open.

   ○ movie   ○ bank   ○ store   ○ library

7 She will _____ the books to the library.

   ○ carry   ○ sell   ○ return   ○ lend   **STOP**

If you play sports, you should drink lots of water. When you get too thirsty, you will not play well. You might even get sick. Drink a little water before you begin, and then drink small amounts of water while you are playing.

S2 **What happens if you play sports and don't drink enough water?**

○ You become sleepy.

⊘ You don't play well.

○ You drink too much water.

When J. R. saw her new house, she wasn't very happy. It was much smaller than her old house, and it was way out in the country.

J. R. and her mother walked around the back of the house.

"Are you the new family here? I'm Willie. I live down the road."

J. R. turned around and saw a boy about her own age. Behind him stood a big brown dog.

"Hi. I'm J. R. and this is my mother.

"Hi. This is my dog, Nick. Say hello, Nick."

The big brown dog walked up to J. R. and put up his paw.

8 **What is this story mostly about?**

○ A boy and his dog

○ A house in the country

⊘ A girl and her new home

9 **Where did J. R. live before?**

● In a bigger house

○ In a smaller house

○ Way out in the country

10 **Why did Nick walk over to J. R. and raise his paw?**

○ He is curious about J. R.

● He is friendly and trained well.

○ He wants to be petted or fed.

GO

Most very large cities have one or more famous museums. Museums are places where people can go to learn about art, science, nature, history, and other subjects. Museums are surprisingly popular. More people go to museums than to professional sporting events.

Art museums are usually quiet places. People go there to study paintings, statues, and other forms of art. In an art museum, pictures are often grouped together in collections because they were made by the same artist or were painted in a similar style.

Science museums are more active places. They have exhibits that show how things work and explain the mysteries of science. People like science museums because they get to try many wonderful experiments.

Natural history museums show the many wonders of nature, such as rocks, gems, animals, and plants. Almost every natural history museum has a display of dinosaurs. This is usually the most popular part of the museum because children and adults love dinosaurs.

11 **Where are famous museums most often found?**

○ In foreign countries

◉ In very large cities

○ In the suburbs

12 **Which of these would be found in a natural history museum?**

◉ An exhibit about wild horses

○ The paintings of Georgia O'Keeffe

○ An exhibit about rockets

13 **What is a difference between art and science museums?**

◉ Science museums are quieter.

○ Art museums are more crowded.

○ Art museums are quieter.

14 **In this story, what is a "collection"?**

○ A group of famous pictures

◉ A group of things that were found

○ A group of similar pictures

GO

Oak trees are among the most important trees in the United States. They grow in many places around the country and range in size from a small bush to a giant tree over a hundred feet tall. Oaks grow wild in forests, and they are also a popular tree for home gardens.

The wood of oak trees is used for building furniture. It is a hard wood that has a beautiful grain. People like oak furniture because it is sturdy and looks pretty. Antique furniture that is made of oak is very valuable even though it might be several hundred years old.

Oak trees produce a nut called an acorn. Animals and birds love to eat acorns. Squirrels and jays often bury acorns and come back for them later. They sometimes forget where they buried the acorns, and from the acorns grow more oak trees.

15 What is this story mostly about?

- Oak trees
- Important trees
- Using trees

16 In this story, what does "antique" mean?

- Something very sturdy
- Something very old
- Something very beautiful

17 What is an acorn most like?

- The root of a sunflower
- The leaf of an apple tree
- The seed of a tomato plant

18 How do jays help oak trees?

- They build their nests in oak trees and lay their eggs.
- They love to eat acorns.
- They bury acorns so more trees will grow.

19 Which words describe what oak wood looks like?

- Beautiful grain
- Valuable
- Several hundred

STOP

Test Practice
Test 4 **Listening**

S

 ○    ○    ○

1

 ○    ○    ○

2

 ○    ○    ○

3

 ○   ○   ○   **GO**

4

PLAY ALL DAY

PAD	PAY	LAD
○	○	○

5

○	○	○

6

○	○	○

7

○	○	○

Test Practice
Test 5 Language

S1

◯ ◯ ◯

1

◯ ◯ ◯

2

◯ ◯ ◯

3

◯ ◯ ◯

GO

4

inch	mile	ruler	yard
○	○	○	○

5

by	with	on	catch
○	○	○	○

S2

were	busy	daye
○	○	○

6

bus	parkd	street
○	○	○

7

dinner	servd	o'clock
○	○	○

8

gaim	started	time
○	○	○

GO

9

said   kitten   hideing
○   ○   ○

10

large   flew   rivir
○   ○   ○

11

frend   visit   month
○   ○   ○

12

walked   botom   hill
○   ○   ○

13

puppy   playd   stick
○   ○   ○

14

tire   tiny   hoal
○   ○   ○

GO →

S3

- ○ Mrs. Ward's first name
- ○ is Katharine, but her friends
- ● usually call her kat.

17

- ● Lisa and sue read books
- ○ by the same authors. The girls
- ○ gave reports on them in class.

15

- ○ On Friday, Dad called
- ● dr. Anderson's office. He
- ○ needed to see the dentist.

18

- ○ Dad took us out for
- ○ French toast at the downtown
- ● breakfast shop on front street.

16

- ○ We visited Aunt Bess.
- ○ She lives near a train station
- ● in the middle of mississippi.

19

- ○ Vic liked meeting other dog
- ● owners. he'd begin by saying,
- ○ "What is your dog's name?"

GO ➡

S4

○   What time will we leave.

○ I want to be sure to get to the

○ train station on time.

22

○   I borrow many things from

○ Mr. Covington He has a

○ great collection of yard tools.

20

○   Pete Janes has a nickname.

○ We call him PJ because those

○ are the first letters of his name.

23

○   Zach was tickling Mick in

○ the backseat of the car. Their

○ mother said, Please stop that.

21

○   My parents were married

○ on March 14 1989. One year

○ later, my oldest sister was born.

24

○   How late is the library

○ open on Saturdays we should

○ call before we get into the car.

GO ➡

S5

○ This is the first time

⊘ that we has ever had snow

○ in the month of June.

25

⊘ The diver standed on the

○ diving board. The crowds of

○ people watched and waited.

26

○ The homework for math

○ was harder than we expected.

⊘ I and Bill studied together.

27

⊘ That there gas station is

○ the oldest one in town. It was

○ there before Grandpa was born.

28

○ Dave helped pick berries.

○ He ignored the small ones in

⊘ favor of the more bigger ones.

29

⊘ We had went to your

○ house, but no one was home.

○ We decided to wait for you.

STOP

Test Practice
Test 6 **Mathematics Concepts**

S

$$4 + 1 + \square = 10$$

5   6   7
○   ○   ○

3

315

○ Three hundred fifty
○ Five hundred thirteen
○ Three hundred fifteen
○ Five hundred thirteen

1

31   39   44   45
○   ○   ○   ○

4

40¢   45¢   50¢   55¢
○   ○   ○   ○

2

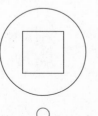

○   ○   ○

5

first   second   third   fourth
○   ○   ○   ○

GO

108

6

10:45   9:10   9:45
  ○   ○   ○

9

58   85   508
 ○   ○   ○

7

$1.23   95¢ $2.95
  ○   ○   ○

10

○ 4 + 2 = 4 + 6

○ 3 + 6 = 6 + 3

○ 3 + 3 = 6 + 2

8

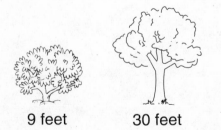

9 feet   30 feet

11   21   29   39
 ○   ○   ○   ○

11

  ○   ○   ○

12

twenty-one

12   20   21
○   ○   ⦸

13

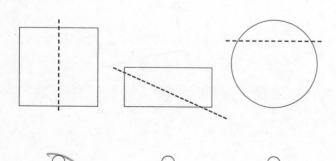

○   ⦸   ○

14

○   ○   ○

15

○ 70 + 210 = ☐ 28
○ 80 + 200 = ☐ 280
○ 80 + 210 = ☐ 29
○ 70 + 200 = ☐

200
70
270

16

	4	7	10	13

1   2   3
⦸   ○   ○

17

○   ○   ○

STOP

S

1	3	6	N
○	○	○	○

3

4	5	8	N
○	○	○	○

1

7	8	9	N
○	○	○	○

4

Boris has 6 fish and 3 birds. He gave 2 fish to his cousin. How many fish did he have left?

1	3	5	N
○	○	○	○

2

3	6	8	N
○	○	○	○

5

Nick wants to make 3 apple pies. He will need 5 apples for each pie. How many apples does Nick need?

8	15	35	N
○	○	○	○

GO ➔

6

Stan had 11 feet of string. He cut off 4 feet and used it to tie up some newspapers. How many feet of string did he have left?

○ $11 + 4 =$ ☐

◐ $11 - 4 =$ ☐

○ $12 - 11 =$ ☐

7

Caryl read 14 pages of her book one morning. She read 9 more pages in the afternoon. How many pages of the book did she read?

○ $14 - 9 =$ ☐

○ $23 - 9 =$ ☐

◐ $14 + 9 =$ ☐

8

Renee spent part of Monday and part of Tuesday studying for a test. How could she find the total amount of time she spent studying?

○ Subtract the number of hours on Monday from those on Tuesday

◐ Add the number of hours on Monday to those on Tuesday

○ Subtract the number of hours on Tuesday from those on Monday

9

Lucas has $10. A basketball usually costs $15. It is on sale for $4 off the regular price. Does Lucas have enough money to buy the basketball?

◐ No, he is $1 short.

○ Yes, he has more than he needs.

◐ Yes, he has exactly what he needs.

 GO

How Many Animals Kayla Saw

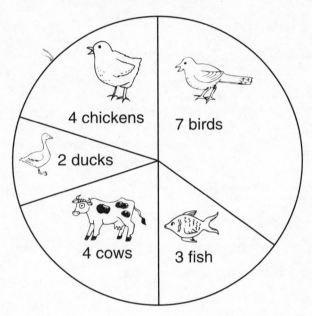

4 chickens

7 birds

2 ducks

4 cows

3 fish

10 Which animal did Kayla see the most of?

○ Cows

⊘ Birds

○ Fish

11 How many cows did Kayla see?

⊘ 4

○ 5

○ 7

12 How many more chickens than ducks did Kayla see?

○ 1

⊘ 2

○ 3

13 Kayla's brother, Horace, saw 2 more fish than Kayla did. How many fish did Horace see?

○ 3

○ 4

⊘ 5

STOP

Test Practice

Test 8 **Mathematics Computation**

S1

1	6	9	N
○	○	○	○

S2 $15 + 4 =$ 19

15	16	17	N
○	○	○	⊘

1

9	11	13	N
○	○	○	○

5 $3 + 6 + 2 + 1 =$

9	11	12	N
○	○	⊘	○

2

9	10	13	N
○	○	○	○

6
$$\begin{array}{r} 301 \\ + 52 \\ \hline \end{array}$$
353

305	315	323	N
○	○	○	⊘

3

10	12	14	N
○	○	○	○

7
$$\begin{array}{r} 12 \\ 8 \\ + 45 \\ \hline \end{array}$$

53	57	65	N
○	○	⊘	○

4

45	54	55	N
○	○	○	○

8
$$\begin{array}{r} 55 \\ + 56 \\ \hline \end{array}$$
111

101	111	115	N
○	⊘	○	○

STOP

9

6	7	9	N
○	○	○	○

14 96 − 15 = 81

80	81	86	N
○	⊘	○	○

10

5	7	8	N
○	○	○	○

15

$$\begin{array}{r} 228 \\ -\ 21 \end{array}$$

207

200	208	220	N
○	○	○	⊘

11

4	7	18	N
○	○	○	○

16

$$\begin{array}{r} 290 \\ -\ 160 \end{array}$$

130

130	160	230	N
⊘	○	○	○

12

13	15	25	N
○	○	○	○

17 341 − 4 = 337

301	330	337	N
○	○	⊘	○

13

11	31	40	N
○	○	○	○

18 83 − 77 = 06

3	6	9	N
○	⊘	○	○

STOP

Guitar

Piano

Bell

Harp

Drum

Whistle

Trumpet

S Which picture should be at the very top of the page?

- ○ Drum
- ○ Bell
- ○ Harp

1 Which picture should be between the harp and the trumpet?

- ○ Guitar
- ○ Whistle
- ○ Piano

2 Which picture should be the third one on the page?

- ○ Drum
- ○ Guitar
- ○ Harp

3 Which picture should be right after the piano?

- ○ Trumpet
- ○ Bell
- ○ Harp

4 Which picture should be between the bell and the guitar?

- ○ Piano
- ○ Trumpet
- ○ Drum

5 Which picture should be the last one on the page?

- ○ Trumpet
- ○ Whistle
- ○ Harp

GO

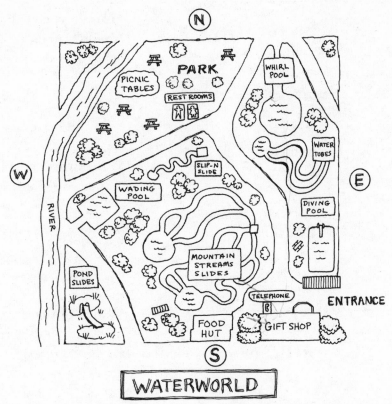

6 **Which is closest to the entrance?**

- ○ The restrooms
- ⊘ The telephones
- ○ The food hut

7 **Which would be the hardest to see from the pond slides?**

- ○ The diving pool
- ○ The river
- ⊘ The wading pool

8 **Which is west of the mountain streams slides?**

- ○ The food hut
- ⊘ The water tubes
- ○ The river

9 **What do you pass first when you go from the gift shop to the park?**

- ○ The diving pool
- ⊘ The mountain streams slides
- ○ The slip-n-slide

10 **Which direction is the whirlpool from the telephones?**

- ○ West
- ○ South
- ⊘ North

11 **Which is in the park?**

- ○ The food hut
- ○ The wading pool
- ⊘ The picnic tables

GO ➡

Test 9 **Sources of Information**

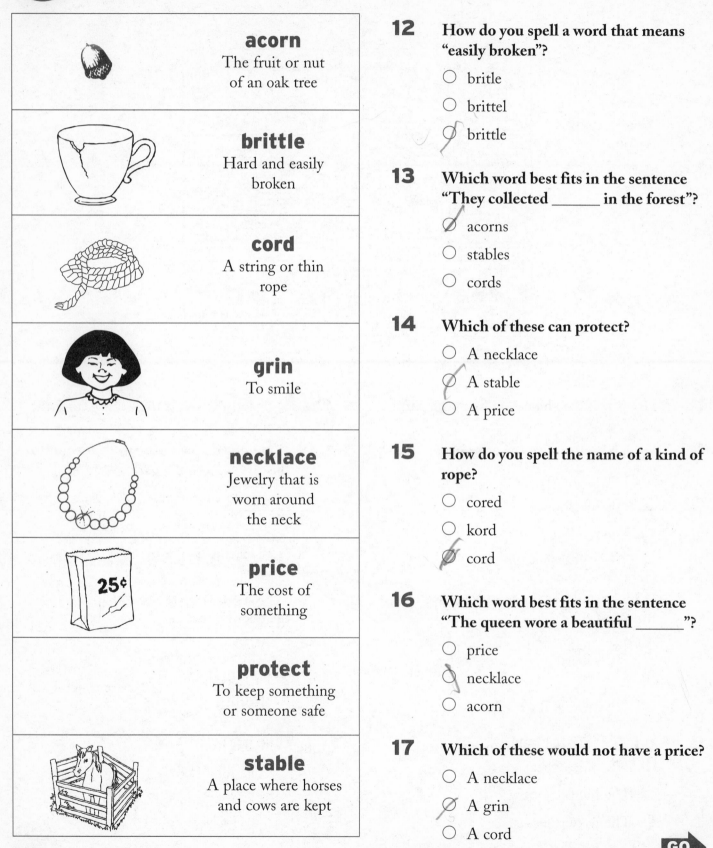

acorn
The fruit or nut of an oak tree

brittle
Hard and easily broken

cord
A string or thin rope

grin
To smile

necklace
Jewelry that is worn around the neck

price
The cost of something

protect
To keep something or someone safe

stable
A place where horses and cows are kept

12 How do you spell a word that means "easily broken"?
- ○ britle
- ○ brittel
- ○ brittle

13 Which word best fits in the sentence "They collected _____ in the forest"?
- ○ acorns
- ○ stables
- ○ cords

14 Which of these can protect?
- ○ A necklace
- ○ A stable
- ○ A price

15 How do you spell the name of a kind of rope?
- ○ cored
- ○ kord
- ○ cord

16 Which word best fits in the sentence "The queen wore a beautiful _____"?
- ○ price
- ○ necklace
- ○ acorn

17 Which of these would not have a price?
- ○ A necklace
- ○ A grin
- ○ A cord

GO ➡

Test 9 **Sources of Information**

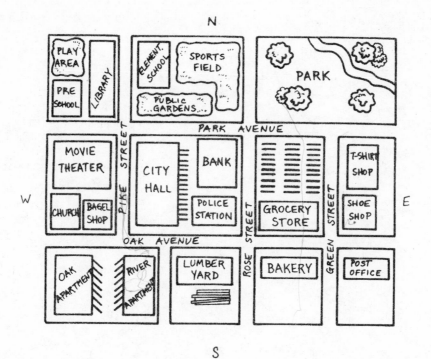

18 **How far is the shoe shop from the park?**

○ One block

○ Two blocks

⊘ Three blocks

19 **Which buildings are across the street from each other?**

○ The library and the elementary school

○ The movie theater and the bakery

○ The lumberyard and the bank

20 **What is closest to the bank?**

○ The movie theater

⊘ The public gardens

○ The oak apartment

21 **Which direction is the bakery from the park?**

○ South

○ West

⊘ East

22 **When Annie leaves the river apartment and goes north on Pike Street, which does she pass first?**

○ The movie theater

○ The public gardens

⊘ City Hall

23 **Which is on Park Avenue?**

○ The post office

○ The movie theater

○ The bagel shop

Emaan's and brothers and sisters
workbook

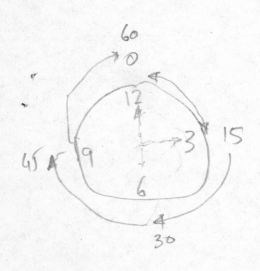

60
0

12

3 15

45 9

6

30

6   7
← 60min →